KU-140-164

Licensed exclusively to Top That Publishing Ltd
Tide Mill Way, Woodbridge, Suffolk, IP12 1AP, UK
www.topthatpublishing.com

0 2 4 6 8 9 7 5 3 1
Printed and bound in China

ISBN 978-1-78244-957-7

A catalogue record for this book is available from the British Library

The Christmas Nativity Tale

A long, long time ago, a woman called Mary was visited by an angel. The angel told Mary that she had been chosen to have a very special baby. The baby was the son of God, and would be called Jesus.

Later that year, the King announced that there would be a census and everyone in the land must return to their place of birth. So Mary and her husband Joseph had to travel from Nazareth to Bethlehem.

The journey was very long and tiring and Mary was going to have her baby very soon. Mary travelled most of the journey on a donkey, led by Joseph.

That night, three wise men were studying the stars when they noticed a new, bright star shining in the sky. The wise men had been waiting a long time for this night; they knew that this meant a very special baby was going to be born.

So, the wise men followed the star and began their great journey to Bethlehem.

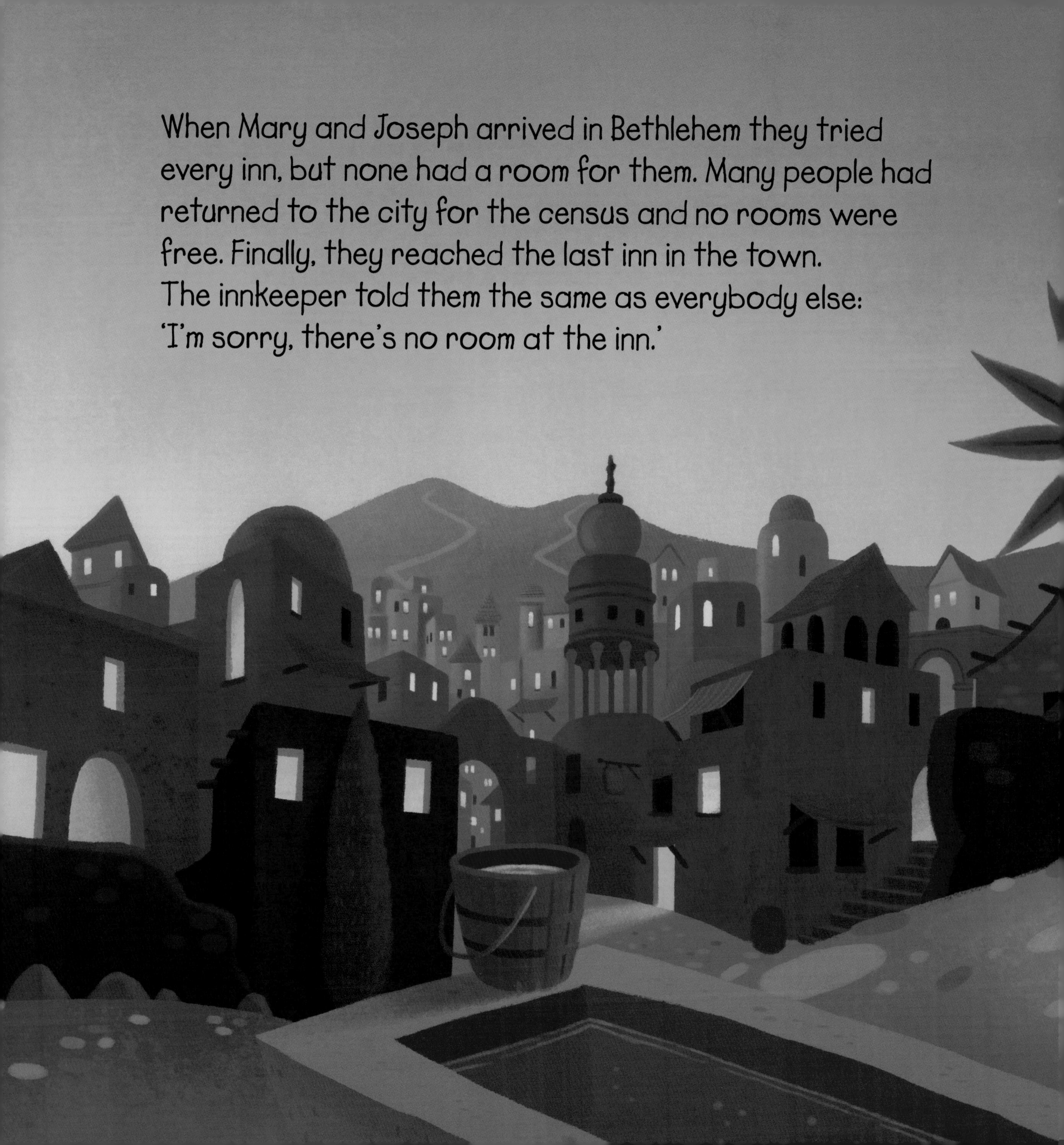

When Mary and Joseph arrived in Bethlehem they tried every inn, but none had a room for them. Many people had returned to the city for the census and no rooms were free. Finally, they reached the last inn in the town. The innkeeper told them the same as everybody else: 'I'm sorry, there's no room at the inn.'

Mary and Joseph were very upset as they had nowhere for Mary to have her baby. The kind innkeeper told them that although he had no rooms spare, they could stay in his stable with the animals.

Also that night, three shepherds were tending their flock on a hill far away from Bethlehem. Suddenly, a burst of light lit up the sky and an angel appeared in front of them. The angel told the shepherds of a very special baby to be born in Bethlehem, and that he was the son of God.

So, the shepherds began their journey to Bethlehem.

That night, in the stable, Mary gave birth to a baby boy and Jesus was born! Mary and Joseph wrapped Jesus in a blanket and placed him in a manger filled with straw, as they had no cradle.

When the three wise men arrived at the stable, they saw Jesus lying in the manger and knew that he would be a leader of men, the King of Kings. The wise men each gave a gift to Jesus – gold, frankincense and myrrh – and then knelt before the baby and worshipped him.

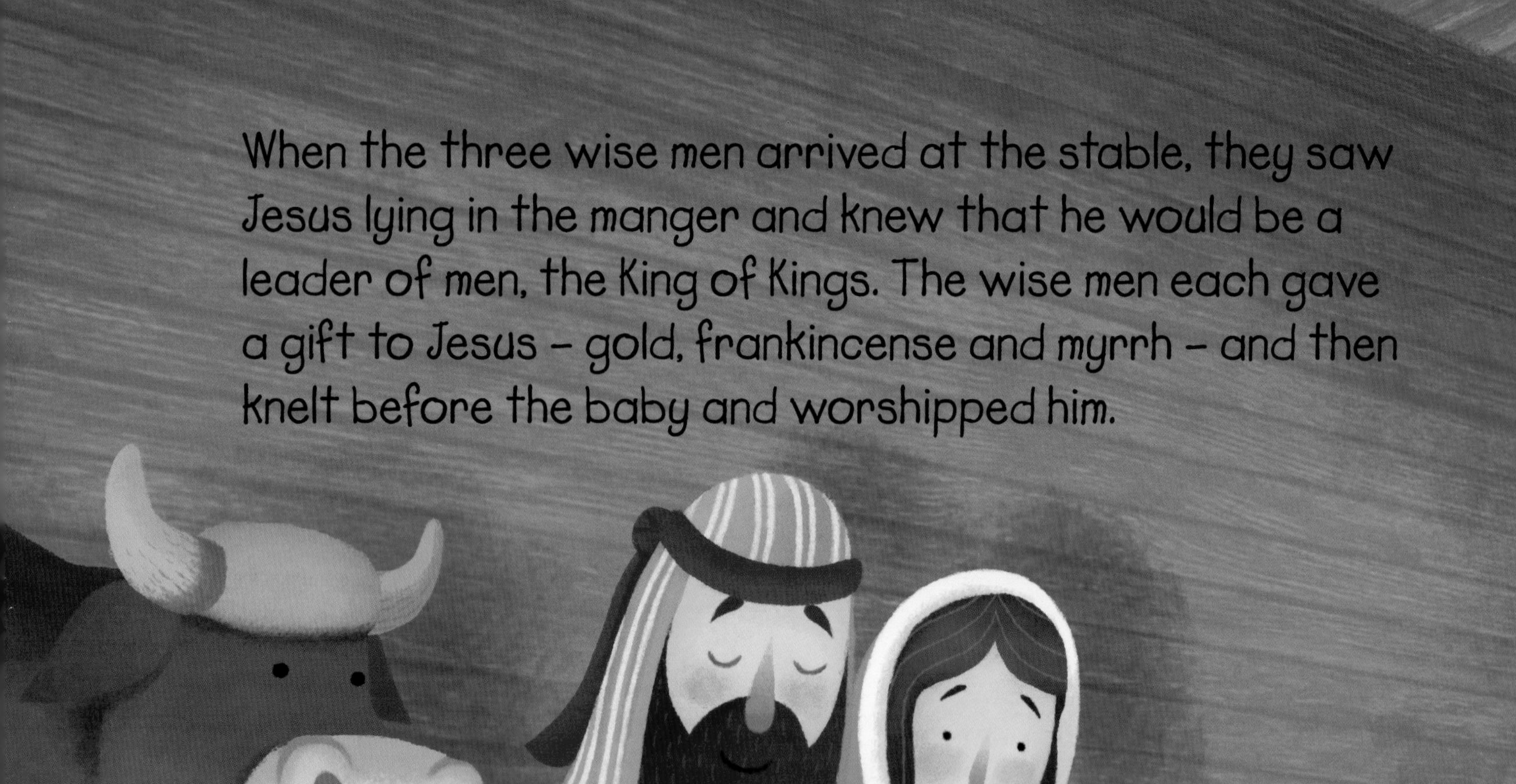

When the shepherds arrived at the stable, they told Mary and Joseph what the angel had told them and they knelt before the baby and worshipped him. Jesus was the son of God, and would grow up to be mankind's saviour.